SERMON NOTES JOURNAL

for Kids ages 9-12

www.wildrose-media.com

ISBN: 978-1-953489-13-5
Copyright ©2020 Wildrose Media. USA.

SERMON NOTEBOOKS FOR YOUNGER KIDS

Simple Sermon Notes for Kids ages 6-8

ISBN: 978-1-953489-09-8

ISBN: 978-1-953489-14-2

AVAILABLE ON AMAZON

www.wildrose-media.com

email: wildrosemedia18@gmail.com

SERMON NOTES JOURNAL

for Kids ages 9-12

THIS BOOK BELONGS TO

_____

_____

_____

www.wildrose-media.com

A WORD ABOUT CHURCH

Did you know that the church is more than just a building? The bible tells us that everyone who believes in Jesus Christ as their Savior is a part of the body of Christ, also known as the church, or body of believers. This includes you!

Christians go to church for many reasons- to learn about God, to praise and worship Him, to pray together as a group, and to spend time with people who also love God. You may find some parts of attending church (such as singing or playing with friends) more enjoyable than others (such as sitting quietly during the sermon). As you learn and grow in faith it is my hope you will look forward to and enjoy church service!

THE PURPOSE OF THIS BOOK

This journal will encourage you to listen and pay attention during the sermon. As you listen, writing down the main points of the sermon will help you remember what was taught. Having sermon notes is helpful- as a reminder for yourself to reflect upon during the week, or to use as you teach others about Jesus.

HOW TO USE THIS BOOK

Take this book with you to church, along with a pencil (and colored pencils or crayons if you'd like). This book has enough pages to journal one full year (52 weeks) of church services and sermons. You will use two pages each week for your notes and activities. Your younger brothers, sisters, cousins, and friends may like the *Simple Sermon Notebook for 6 to 8-year old's*, also published by Wildrose Media (sample pages are provided in the front of this book, see the back page of this book for additional books available on Amazon).

To begin, write down the date, sermon title, and scripture passage for the day. As the service begins, take note of the songs which are sung and write down your favorite, or favorites.

Take a moment to look over the list of words which you are to listen for during today's sermon. Decide if you will check the words off only once OR each time you hear the word- either choice is fine, it is up to you. An important note -depending on the sermon topic for the week, some words may not be used at all, this is okay!

Use the lines provided to write your sermon notes. These notes should include the important points the pastor is preaching on, with additional notes to help you remember what was taught. If you have questions or hear words you don't understand, write them down so you can look them up or ask someone about them later. For those people who listen better while drawing or doodling, a space for creative worship has been provided. The drawing space may be used at home, after the church service if you prefer.

Use the prayer box to write down the prayer requests mentioned during service or in the church bulletin and then add your own. Use the thankful box for answered prayers and gratitude to God- you may also wish to add to the prayer and thanksgiving boxes during the week- so keep this journal nearby!

After the service, take a moment to summarize what the sermon's message was. Ask yourself, is there anything I should change or do differently in my own life as a result of hearing today's sermon? Decide to do it!

Share what you learned with others. Do you know anyone who may benefit from hearing about today's message? If so, find an opportunity to share it with them. Use your sermon notes to help you teach them.

DATE:

MY FAVORITE SONG TODAY:

WORDS I DID NOT UNDERSTAND:

I AM THANKFUL FOR:

THIS WEEK, I WILL PRAY FOR:

TODAY'S SCRIPTURE PASSAGE:

I LEFT CHURCH FEELING:

THIS WEEK, I WILL:
(write something you learned today that you can apply to your life this week)

CREATIVE SPACE

WORDS I HEARD THE PASTOR SAY:
(CHECK ONCE OR EACH TIME YOU HEAR IT)

- ○ God
- ○ Jesus
- ○ Holy Spirit
- ○ Church
- ○ Disciples
- ○ Pray
- ○ Love
- ○ Worship
- ○ Joy
- ○ Repent

- ○ Believe
- ○ Faith
- ○ Bible
- ○ World
- ○ Father
- ○ Son
- ○ Amen
- ○ Grace
- ○ Saved
- ○ Sin

QUESTIONS I HAVE:

SERMON TITLE:

SERMON NOTES:

DATE:

MY FAVORITE SONG TODAY:

WORDS I DID NOT UNDERSTAND:

I AM THANKFUL FOR:

THIS WEEK, I WILL PRAY FOR:

TODAY'S SCRIPTURE PASSAGE:

I LEFT CHURCH FEELING:

THIS WEEK, I WILL:
(write something you learned today that you can apply to your life this week)

CREATIVE SPACE

WORDS I HEARD THE PASTOR SAY:
(CHECK ONCE OR EACH TIME YOU HEAR IT)

- o God
- o Jesus
- o Holy Spirit
- o Church
- o Disciples
- o Pray
- o Love
- o Worship
- o Joy
- o Repent

- o Believe
- o Faith
- o Bible
- o World
- o Father
- o Son
- o Amen
- o Grace
- o Saved
- o Sin

QUESTIONS I HAVE:

SERMON TITLE:

SERMON NOTES:

DATE:

MY FAVORITE SONG TODAY:

WORDS I DID NOT UNDERSTAND:

I AM THANKFUL FOR:

THIS WEEK, I WILL PRAY FOR:

TODAY'S SCRIPTURE PASSAGE:

I LEFT CHURCH FEELING:

THIS WEEK, I WILL:
(write something you learned today that you can apply to your life this week)

CREATIVE SPACE

WORDS I HEARD THE PASTOR SAY:
(CHECK ONCE OR EACH TIME YOU HEAR IT)

- ○ God
- ○ Jesus
- ○ Holy Spirit
- ○ Church
- ○ Disciples
- ○ Pray
- ○ Love
- ○ Worship
- ○ Joy
- ○ Repent

- ○ Believe
- ○ Faith
- ○ Bible
- ○ World
- ○ Father
- ○ Son
- ○ Amen
- ○ Grace
- ○ Saved
- ○ Sin

QUESTIONS I HAVE:

SERMON TITLE:

SERMON NOTES:

DATE:

MY FAVORITE SONG TODAY:

WORDS I DID NOT UNDERSTAND:

I AM THANKFUL FOR:

THIS WEEK, I WILL PRAY FOR:

TODAY'S SCRIPTURE PASSAGE:

I LEFT CHURCH FEELING:

THIS WEEK, I WILL:
(write something you learned today that you can apply to your life this week)

CREATIVE SPACE

WORDS I HEARD THE PASTOR SAY:
(CHECK ONCE OR EACH TIME YOU HEAR IT)

- ○ God
- ○ Jesus
- ○ Holy Spirit
- ○ Church
- ○ Disciples
- ○ Pray
- ○ Love
- ○ Worship
- ○ Joy
- ○ Repent

- ○ Believe
- ○ Faith
- ○ Bible
- ○ World
- ○ Father
- ○ Son
- ○ Amen
- ○ Grace
- ○ Saved
- ○ Sin

QUESTIONS I HAVE:

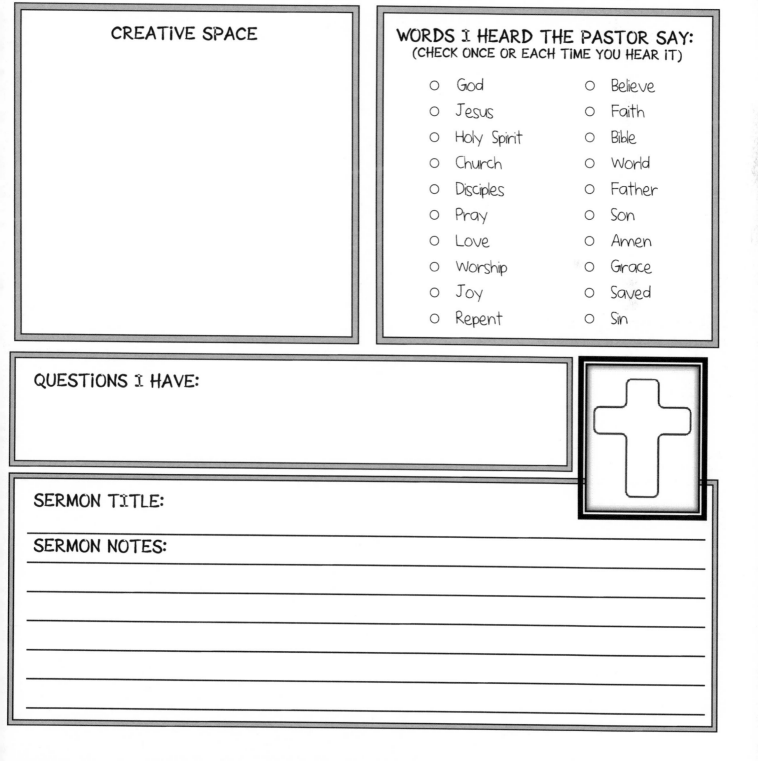

SERMON TITLE:

SERMON NOTES:

DATE:

MY FAVORITE SONG TODAY:

WORDS I DID NOT UNDERSTAND:

I AM THANKFUL FOR:

THIS WEEK, I WILL PRAY FOR:

TODAY'S SCRIPTURE PASSAGE:

I LEFT CHURCH FEELING:

THIS WEEK, I WILL:
(write something you learned today that you can apply to your life this week)

CREATIVE SPACE

WORDS I HEARD THE PASTOR SAY:
(CHECK ONCE OR EACH TIME YOU HEAR IT)

- o God
- o Jesus
- o Holy Spirit
- o Church
- o Disciples
- o Pray
- o Love
- o Worship
- o Joy
- o Repent

- o Believe
- o Faith
- o Bible
- o World
- o Father
- o Son
- o Amen
- o Grace
- o Saved
- o Sin

QUESTIONS I HAVE:

SERMON TITLE:

SERMON NOTES:

DATE:

MY FAVORITE SONG TODAY:

WORDS I DID NOT UNDERSTAND:

I AM THANKFUL FOR:

THIS WEEK, I WILL PRAY FOR:

TODAY'S SCRIPTURE PASSAGE:

I LEFT CHURCH FEELING:

THIS WEEK, I WILL:
(write something you learned today that you can apply to your life this week)

CREATIVE SPACE

WORDS I HEARD THE PASTOR SAY:
(CHECK ONCE OR EACH TIME YOU HEAR IT)

- o God
- o Jesus
- o Holy Spirit
- o Church
- o Disciples
- o Pray
- o Love
- o Worship
- o Joy
- o Repent

- o Believe
- o Faith
- o Bible
- o World
- o Father
- o Son
- o Amen
- o Grace
- o Saved
- o Sin

QUESTIONS I HAVE:

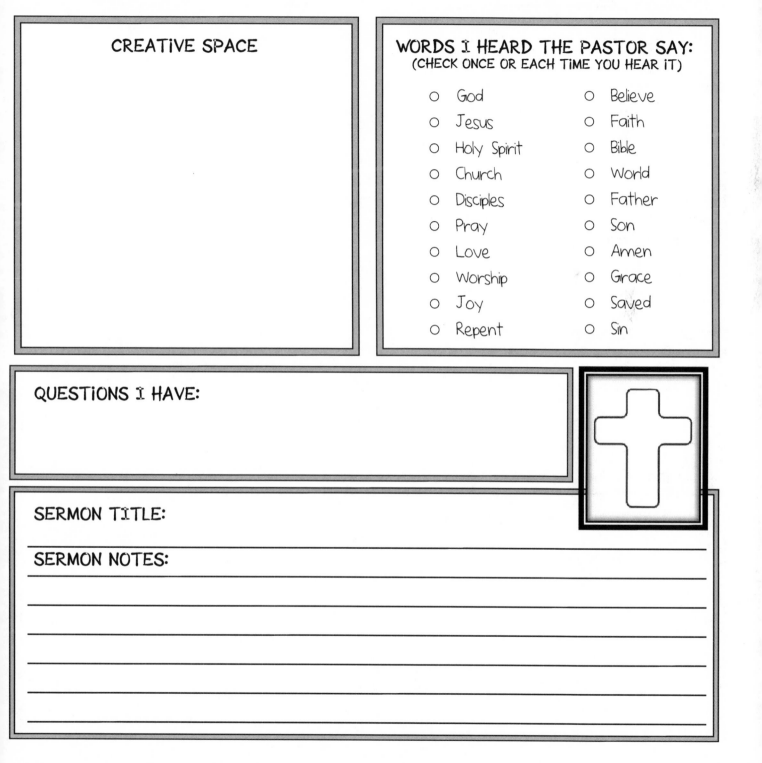

SERMON TITLE:

SERMON NOTES:

DATE:

MY FAVORITE SONG TODAY:

WORDS I DID NOT UNDERSTAND:

I AM THANKFUL FOR:

THIS WEEK, I WILL PRAY FOR:

TODAY'S SCRIPTURE PASSAGE:

I LEFT CHURCH FEELING:

THIS WEEK, I WILL:
(write something you learned today that you can apply to your life this week)

CREATIVE SPACE

WORDS I HEARD THE PASTOR SAY:
(CHECK ONCE OR EACH TIME YOU HEAR iT)

- o God
- o Jesus
- o Holy Spirit
- o Church
- o Disciples
- o Pray
- o Love
- o Worship
- o Joy
- o Repent

- o Believe
- o Faith
- o Bible
- o World
- o Father
- o Son
- o Amen
- o Grace
- o Saved
- o Sin

QUESTIONS I HAVE:

SERMON TITLE:

SERMON NOTES:

DATE:

MY FAVORITE SONG TODAY:

WORDS I DID NOT UNDERSTAND:

I AM THANKFUL FOR:

THIS WEEK, I WILL PRAY FOR:

TODAY'S SCRIPTURE PASSAGE:

I LEFT CHURCH FEELING:

THIS WEEK, I WILL:
(write something you learned today that you can apply to your life this week)

CREATIVE SPACE

WORDS I HEARD THE PASTOR SAY:
(CHECK ONCE OR EACH TIME YOU HEAR IT)

- O God
- O Jesus
- O Holy Spirit
- O Church
- O Disciples
- O Pray
- O Love
- O Worship
- O Joy
- O Repent

- O Believe
- O Faith
- O Bible
- O World
- O Father
- O Son
- O Amen
- O Grace
- O Saved
- O Sin

QUESTIONS I HAVE:

SERMON TITLE:

SERMON NOTES:

DATE:

MY FAVORITE SONG TODAY:

WORDS I DID NOT UNDERSTAND:

I AM THANKFUL FOR:

THIS WEEK, I WILL PRAY FOR:

TODAY'S SCRIPTURE PASSAGE:

I LEFT CHURCH FEELING:

THIS WEEK, I WILL:
(write something you learned today that you can apply to your life this week)

CREATIVE SPACE

WORDS I HEARD THE PASTOR SAY:
(CHECK ONCE OR EACH TIME YOU HEAR IT)

- ○ God
- ○ Jesus
- ○ Holy Spirit
- ○ Church
- ○ Disciples
- ○ Pray
- ○ Love
- ○ Worship
- ○ Joy
- ○ Repent

- ○ Believe
- ○ Faith
- ○ Bible
- ○ World
- ○ Father
- ○ Son
- ○ Amen
- ○ Grace
- ○ Saved
- ○ Sin

QUESTIONS I HAVE:

SERMON TITLE:

SERMON NOTES:

DATE:

MY FAVORITE SONG TODAY:

WORDS I DID NOT UNDERSTAND:

I AM THANKFUL FOR:

THIS WEEK, I WILL PRAY FOR:

TODAY'S SCRIPTURE PASSAGE:

I LEFT CHURCH FEELING:

THIS WEEK, I WILL:
(write something you learned today that you can apply to your life this week)

CREATIVE SPACE

WORDS I HEARD THE PASTOR SAY:
(CHECK ONCE OR EACH TIME YOU HEAR IT)

- ○ God
- ○ Jesus
- ○ Holy Spirit
- ○ Church
- ○ Disciples
- ○ Pray
- ○ Love
- ○ Worship
- ○ Joy
- ○ Repent

- ○ Believe
- ○ Faith
- ○ Bible
- ○ World
- ○ Father
- ○ Son
- ○ Amen
- ○ Grace
- ○ Saved
- ○ Sin

QUESTIONS I HAVE:

SERMON TITLE:

SERMON NOTES:

DATE:

MY FAVORITE SONG TODAY:

WORDS I DID NOT UNDERSTAND:

I AM THANKFUL FOR:

THIS WEEK, I WILL PRAY FOR:

TODAY'S SCRIPTURE PASSAGE:

I LEFT CHURCH FEELING:

THIS WEEK, I WILL:
(write something you learned today that you can apply to your life this week)

CREATIVE SPACE

WORDS I HEARD THE PASTOR SAY:
(CHECK ONCE OR EACH TIME YOU HEAR IT)

- ○ God
- ○ Jesus
- ○ Holy Spirit
- ○ Church
- ○ Disciples
- ○ Pray
- ○ Love
- ○ Worship
- ○ Joy
- ○ Repent
- ○ Believe
- ○ Faith
- ○ Bible
- ○ World
- ○ Father
- ○ Son
- ○ Amen
- ○ Grace
- ○ Saved
- ○ Sin

QUESTIONS I HAVE:

SERMON TITLE:

SERMON NOTES:

DATE:

MY FAVORITE SONG TODAY:

WORDS I DID NOT UNDERSTAND:

I AM THANKFUL FOR:

THIS WEEK, I WILL PRAY FOR:

TODAY'S SCRIPTURE PASSAGE:

I LEFT CHURCH FEELING:

THIS WEEK, I WILL:
(write something you learned today that you can apply to your life this week)

CREATIVE SPACE

WORDS I HEARD THE PASTOR SAY:
(CHECK ONCE OR EACH TIME YOU HEAR IT)

- ○ God
- ○ Jesus
- ○ Holy Spirit
- ○ Church
- ○ Disciples
- ○ Pray
- ○ Love
- ○ Worship
- ○ Joy
- ○ Repent

- ○ Believe
- ○ Faith
- ○ Bible
- ○ World
- ○ Father
- ○ Son
- ○ Amen
- ○ Grace
- ○ Saved
- ○ Sin

QUESTIONS I HAVE:

SERMON TITLE:

SERMON NOTES:

DATE:

MY FAVORITE SONG TODAY:

WORDS I DID NOT UNDERSTAND:

I AM THANKFUL FOR:

THIS WEEK, I WILL PRAY FOR:

TODAY'S SCRIPTURE PASSAGE:

I LEFT CHURCH FEELING:

THIS WEEK, I WILL:
(write something you learned today that you can apply to your life this week)

CREATIVE SPACE

WORDS I HEARD THE PASTOR SAY:
(CHECK ONCE OR EACH TIME YOU HEAR IT)

- o God
- o Jesus
- o Holy Spirit
- o Church
- o Disciples
- o Pray
- o Love
- o Worship
- o Joy
- o Repent

- o Believe
- o Faith
- o Bible
- o World
- o Father
- o Son
- o Amen
- o Grace
- o Saved
- o Sin

QUESTIONS I HAVE:

SERMON TITLE:

SERMON NOTES:

DATE:

MY FAVORITE SONG TODAY:

WORDS I DID NOT UNDERSTAND:

I AM THANKFUL FOR:

THIS WEEK, I WILL PRAY FOR:

TODAY'S SCRIPTURE PASSAGE:

I LEFT CHURCH FEELING:

THIS WEEK, I WILL:
(write something you learned today that you can apply to your life this week)

CREATIVE SPACE

WORDS I HEARD THE PASTOR SAY:
(CHECK ONCE OR EACH TIME YOU HEAR IT)

- o God
- o Jesus
- o Holy Spirit
- o Church
- o Disciples
- o Pray
- o Love
- o Worship
- o Joy
- o Repent

- o Believe
- o Faith
- o Bible
- o World
- o Father
- o Son
- o Amen
- o Grace
- o Saved
- o Sin

QUESTIONS I HAVE:

SERMON TITLE:

SERMON NOTES:

DATE:

MY FAVORITE SONG TODAY:

WORDS I DID NOT UNDERSTAND:

I AM THANKFUL FOR:

THIS WEEK, I WILL PRAY FOR:

TODAY'S SCRIPTURE PASSAGE:

I LEFT CHURCH FEELING:

THIS WEEK, I WILL:
(write something you learned today that you can apply to your life this week)

CREATIVE SPACE

WORDS I HEARD THE PASTOR SAY:
(CHECK ONCE OR EACH TIME YOU HEAR IT)

- o God
- o Jesus
- o Holy Spirit
- o Church
- o Disciples
- o Pray
- o Love
- o Worship
- o Joy
- o Repent

- o Believe
- o Faith
- o Bible
- o World
- o Father
- o Son
- o Amen
- o Grace
- o Saved
- o Sin

QUESTIONS I HAVE:

SERMON TITLE:

SERMON NOTES:

DATE:

MY FAVORITE SONG TODAY:

WORDS I DID NOT UNDERSTAND:

I AM THANKFUL FOR:

THIS WEEK, I WILL PRAY FOR:

TODAY'S SCRIPTURE PASSAGE:

I LEFT CHURCH FEELING:

THIS WEEK, I WILL:
(write something you learned today that you can apply to your life this week)

CREATIVE SPACE

WORDS I HEARD THE PASTOR SAY:
(CHECK ONCE OR EACH TIME YOU HEAR IT)

- ○ God
- ○ Jesus
- ○ Holy Spirit
- ○ Church
- ○ Disciples
- ○ Pray
- ○ Love
- ○ Worship
- ○ Joy
- ○ Repent

- ○ Believe
- ○ Faith
- ○ Bible
- ○ World
- ○ Father
- ○ Son
- ○ Amen
- ○ Grace
- ○ Saved
- ○ Sin

QUESTIONS I HAVE:

SERMON TITLE:

SERMON NOTES:

DATE:

MY FAVORITE SONG TODAY:

WORDS I DID NOT UNDERSTAND:

I AM THANKFUL FOR:

THIS WEEK, I WILL PRAY FOR:

TODAY'S SCRIPTURE PASSAGE:

I LEFT CHURCH FEELING:

THIS WEEK, I WILL:
(write something you learned today that you can apply to your life this week)

CREATIVE SPACE

WORDS I HEARD THE PASTOR SAY:
(CHECK ONCE OR EACH TIME YOU HEAR IT)

- ○ God
- ○ Jesus
- ○ Holy Spirit
- ○ Church
- ○ Disciples
- ○ Pray
- ○ Love
- ○ Worship
- ○ Joy
- ○ Repent

- ○ Believe
- ○ Faith
- ○ Bible
- ○ World
- ○ Father
- ○ Son
- ○ Amen
- ○ Grace
- ○ Saved
- ○ Sin

QUESTIONS I HAVE:

SERMON TITLE:

SERMON NOTES:

DATE:

MY FAVORITE SONG TODAY:

WORDS I DID NOT UNDERSTAND:

I AM THANKFUL FOR:

THIS WEEK, I WILL PRAY FOR:

TODAY'S SCRIPTURE PASSAGE:

I LEFT CHURCH FEELING:

THIS WEEK, I WILL:
(write something you learned today that you can apply to your life this week)

CREATIVE SPACE

WORDS I HEARD THE PASTOR SAY:
(CHECK ONCE OR EACH TIME YOU HEAR IT)

○ God	○ Believe
○ Jesus	○ Faith
○ Holy Spirit	○ Bible
○ Church	○ World
○ Disciples	○ Father
○ Pray	○ Son
○ Love	○ Amen
○ Worship	○ Grace
○ Joy	○ Saved
○ Repent	○ Sin

QUESTIONS I HAVE:

SERMON TITLE:

SERMON NOTES:

DATE:

MY FAVORITE SONG TODAY:

WORDS I DID NOT UNDERSTAND:

I AM THANKFUL FOR:

THIS WEEK, I WILL PRAY FOR:

TODAY'S SCRIPTURE PASSAGE:

I LEFT CHURCH FEELING:

THIS WEEK, I WILL:
(write something you learned today that you can apply to your life this week)

CREATIVE SPACE

WORDS I HEARD THE PASTOR SAY:
(CHECK ONCE OR EACH TIME YOU HEAR IT)

- O God
- O Jesus
- O Holy Spirit
- O Church
- O Disciples
- O Pray
- O Love
- O Worship
- O Joy
- O Repent

- O Believe
- O Faith
- O Bible
- O World
- O Father
- O Son
- O Amen
- O Grace
- O Saved
- O Sin

QUESTIONS I HAVE:

SERMON TITLE:

SERMON NOTES:

DATE:

MY FAVORITE SONG TODAY:

WORDS I DID NOT UNDERSTAND:

I AM THANKFUL FOR:

THIS WEEK, I WILL PRAY FOR:

TODAY'S SCRIPTURE PASSAGE:

I LEFT CHURCH FEELING:

THIS WEEK, I WILL:
(write something you learned today that you can apply to your life this week)

CREATIVE SPACE

WORDS I HEARD THE PASTOR SAY:
(CHECK ONCE OR EACH TIME YOU HEAR IT)

- ○ God
- ○ Jesus
- ○ Holy Spirit
- ○ Church
- ○ Disciples
- ○ Pray
- ○ Love
- ○ Worship
- ○ Joy
- ○ Repent

- ○ Believe
- ○ Faith
- ○ Bible
- ○ World
- ○ Father
- ○ Son
- ○ Amen
- ○ Grace
- ○ Saved
- ○ Sin

QUESTIONS I HAVE:

SERMON TITLE:

SERMON NOTES:

DATE:

MY FAVORITE SONG TODAY:

WORDS I DID NOT UNDERSTAND:

I AM THANKFUL FOR:

THIS WEEK, I WILL PRAY FOR:

TODAY'S SCRIPTURE PASSAGE:

I LEFT CHURCH FEELING:

THIS WEEK, I WILL:
(write something you learned today that you can apply to your life this week)

CREATIVE SPACE

WORDS I HEARD THE PASTOR SAY:
(CHECK ONCE OR EACH TIME YOU HEAR IT)

- o God
- o Jesus
- o Holy Spirit
- o Church
- o Disciples
- o Pray
- o Love
- o Worship
- o Joy
- o Repent

- o Believe
- o Faith
- o Bible
- o World
- o Father
- o Son
- o Amen
- o Grace
- o Saved
- o Sin

QUESTIONS I HAVE:

SERMON TITLE:

SERMON NOTES:

DATE:

MY FAVORITE SONG TODAY:

WORDS I DID NOT UNDERSTAND:

I AM THANKFUL FOR:

THIS WEEK, I WILL PRAY FOR:

TODAY'S SCRIPTURE PASSAGE:

I LEFT CHURCH FEELING:

THIS WEEK, I WILL:
(write something you learned today that
you can apply to your life this week)

CREATIVE SPACE

WORDS I HEARD THE PASTOR SAY:
(CHECK ONCE OR EACH TIME YOU HEAR IT)

- ○ God
- ○ Jesus
- ○ Holy Spirit
- ○ Church
- ○ Disciples
- ○ Pray
- ○ Love
- ○ Worship
- ○ Joy
- ○ Repent

- ○ Believe
- ○ Faith
- ○ Bible
- ○ World
- ○ Father
- ○ Son
- ○ Amen
- ○ Grace
- ○ Saved
- ○ Sin

QUESTIONS I HAVE:

SERMON TITLE:

SERMON NOTES:

DATE:

MY FAVORITE SONG TODAY:

WORDS I DID NOT UNDERSTAND:

I AM THANKFUL FOR:

THIS WEEK, I WILL PRAY FOR:

TODAY'S SCRIPTURE PASSAGE:

I LEFT CHURCH FEELING:

THIS WEEK, I WILL:
(write something you learned today that you can apply to your life this week)

CREATIVE SPACE

WORDS I HEARD THE PASTOR SAY:
(CHECK ONCE OR EACH TIME YOU HEAR IT)

- ○ God
- ○ Jesus
- ○ Holy Spirit
- ○ Church
- ○ Disciples
- ○ Pray
- ○ Love
- ○ Worship
- ○ Joy
- ○ Repent
- ○ Believe
- ○ Faith
- ○ Bible
- ○ World
- ○ Father
- ○ Son
- ○ Amen
- ○ Grace
- ○ Saved
- ○ Sin

QUESTIONS I HAVE:

SERMON TITLE:

SERMON NOTES:

DATE:

MY FAVORITE SONG TODAY:

WORDS I DID NOT UNDERSTAND:

I AM THANKFUL FOR:

THIS WEEK, I WILL PRAY FOR:

TODAY'S SCRIPTURE PASSAGE:

I LEFT CHURCH FEELING:

THIS WEEK, I WILL:
(write something you learned today that you can apply to your life this week)

CREATIVE SPACE

WORDS I HEARD THE PASTOR SAY:
(CHECK ONCE OR EACH TIME YOU HEAR IT)

- ○ God
- ○ Jesus
- ○ Holy Spirit
- ○ Church
- ○ Disciples
- ○ Pray
- ○ Love
- ○ Worship
- ○ Joy
- ○ Repent

- ○ Believe
- ○ Faith
- ○ Bible
- ○ World
- ○ Father
- ○ Son
- ○ Amen
- ○ Grace
- ○ Saved
- ○ Sin

QUESTIONS I HAVE:

SERMON TITLE:

SERMON NOTES:

DATE:

MY FAVORITE SONG TODAY:

WORDS I DID NOT UNDERSTAND:

I AM THANKFUL FOR:

THIS WEEK, I WILL PRAY FOR:

TODAY'S SCRIPTURE PASSAGE:

I LEFT CHURCH FEELING:

THIS WEEK, I WILL:
(write something you learned today that you can apply to your life this week)

CREATIVE SPACE

WORDS I HEARD THE PASTOR SAY:
(CHECK ONCE OR EACH TIME YOU HEAR IT)

- ○ God
- ○ Jesus
- ○ Holy Spirit
- ○ Church
- ○ Disciples
- ○ Pray
- ○ Love
- ○ Worship
- ○ Joy
- ○ Repent

- ○ Believe
- ○ Faith
- ○ Bible
- ○ World
- ○ Father
- ○ Son
- ○ Amen
- ○ Grace
- ○ Saved
- ○ Sin

QUESTIONS I HAVE:

SERMON TITLE:

SERMON NOTES:

DATE:

MY FAVORITE SONG TODAY:

WORDS I DID NOT UNDERSTAND:

I AM THANKFUL FOR:

THIS WEEK, I WILL PRAY FOR:

TODAY'S SCRIPTURE PASSAGE:

I LEFT CHURCH FEELING:

THIS WEEK, I WILL:
(write something you learned today that you can apply to your life this week)

CREATIVE SPACE

WORDS I HEARD THE PASTOR SAY:
(CHECK ONCE OR EACH TIME YOU HEAR IT)

- O God
- O Jesus
- O Holy Spirit
- O Church
- O Disciples
- O Pray
- O Love
- O Worship
- O Joy
- O Repent

- O Believe
- O Faith
- O Bible
- O World
- O Father
- O Son
- O Amen
- O Grace
- O Saved
- O Sin

QUESTIONS I HAVE:

SERMON TITLE:

SERMON NOTES:

DATE:

MY FAVORITE SONG TODAY:

WORDS I DID NOT UNDERSTAND:

I AM THANKFUL FOR:

THIS WEEK, I WILL PRAY FOR:

TODAY'S SCRIPTURE PASSAGE:

I LEFT CHURCH FEELING:

THIS WEEK, I WILL:
(write something you learned today that you can apply to your life this week)

CREATIVE SPACE

WORDS I HEARD THE PASTOR SAY:
(CHECK ONCE OR EACH TIME YOU HEAR IT)

- o God
- o Jesus
- o Holy Spirit
- o Church
- o Disciples
- o Pray
- o Love
- o Worship
- o Joy
- o Repent

- o Believe
- o Faith
- o Bible
- o World
- o Father
- o Son
- o Amen
- o Grace
- o Saved
- o Sin

QUESTIONS I HAVE:

SERMON TITLE:

SERMON NOTES:

DATE:

MY FAVORITE SONG TODAY:

WORDS I DID NOT UNDERSTAND:

I AM THANKFUL FOR:

THIS WEEK, I WILL PRAY FOR:

TODAY'S SCRIPTURE PASSAGE:

I LEFT CHURCH FEELING:

THIS WEEK, I WILL:
(write something you learned today that
you can apply to your life this week)

CREATIVE SPACE

WORDS I HEARD THE PASTOR SAY:
(CHECK ONCE OR EACH TIME YOU HEAR IT)

- ○ God
- ○ Jesus
- ○ Holy Spirit
- ○ Church
- ○ Disciples
- ○ Pray
- ○ Love
- ○ Worship
- ○ Joy
- ○ Repent

- ○ Believe
- ○ Faith
- ○ Bible
- ○ World
- ○ Father
- ○ Son
- ○ Amen
- ○ Grace
- ○ Saved
- ○ Sin

QUESTIONS I HAVE:

SERMON TITLE:

SERMON NOTES:

DATE:

MY FAVORITE SONG TODAY:

WORDS I DID NOT UNDERSTAND:

I AM THANKFUL FOR:

THIS WEEK, I WILL PRAY FOR:

TODAY'S SCRIPTURE PASSAGE:

I LEFT CHURCH FEELING:

THIS WEEK, I WILL:
(write something you learned today that you can apply to your life this week)

CREATIVE SPACE

WORDS I HEARD THE PASTOR SAY:
(CHECK ONCE OR EACH TIME YOU HEAR IT)

- o God
- o Jesus
- o Holy Spirit
- o Church
- o Disciples
- o Pray
- o Love
- o Worship
- o Joy
- o Repent

- o Believe
- o Faith
- o Bible
- o World
- o Father
- o Son
- o Amen
- o Grace
- o Saved
- o Sin

QUESTIONS I HAVE:

SERMON TITLE:

SERMON NOTES:

DATE:

MY FAVORITE SONG TODAY:

WORDS I DID NOT UNDERSTAND:

I AM THANKFUL FOR:

THIS WEEK, I WILL PRAY FOR:

TODAY'S SCRIPTURE PASSAGE:

I LEFT CHURCH FEELING:

THIS WEEK, I WILL:
(write something you learned today that you can apply to your life this week)

CREATIVE SPACE

WORDS I HEARD THE PASTOR SAY:
(CHECK ONCE OR EACH TIME YOU HEAR IT)

- ○ God
- ○ Jesus
- ○ Holy Spirit
- ○ Church
- ○ Disciples
- ○ Pray
- ○ Love
- ○ Worship
- ○ Joy
- ○ Repent

- ○ Believe
- ○ Faith
- ○ Bible
- ○ World
- ○ Father
- ○ Son
- ○ Amen
- ○ Grace
- ○ Saved
- ○ Sin

QUESTIONS I HAVE:

SERMON TITLE:

SERMON NOTES:

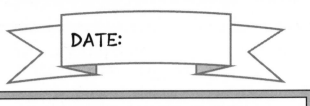

DATE:

MY FAVORITE SONG TODAY:

WORDS I DID NOT UNDERSTAND:

I AM THANKFUL FOR:

THIS WEEK, I WILL PRAY FOR:

TODAY'S SCRIPTURE PASSAGE:

I LEFT CHURCH FEELING:

THIS WEEK, I WILL:
(write something you learned today that you can apply to your life this week)

CREATIVE SPACE

WORDS I HEARD THE PASTOR SAY:
(CHECK ONCE OR EACH TIME YOU HEAR IT)

- ○ God
- ○ Jesus
- ○ Holy Spirit
- ○ Church
- ○ Disciples
- ○ Pray
- ○ Love
- ○ Worship
- ○ Joy
- ○ Repent

- ○ Believe
- ○ Faith
- ○ Bible
- ○ World
- ○ Father
- ○ Son
- ○ Amen
- ○ Grace
- ○ Saved
- ○ Sin

QUESTIONS I HAVE:

SERMON TITLE:

SERMON NOTES:

DATE:

MY FAVORITE SONG TODAY:

WORDS I DID NOT UNDERSTAND:

I AM THANKFUL FOR:

THIS WEEK, I WILL PRAY FOR:

TODAY'S SCRIPTURE PASSAGE:

I LEFT CHURCH FEELING:

THIS WEEK, I WILL:
(write something you learned today that you can apply to your life this week)

CREATIVE SPACE

WORDS I HEARD THE PASTOR SAY:
(CHECK ONCE OR EACH TIME YOU HEAR IT)

- o God
- o Jesus
- o Holy Spirit
- o Church
- o Disciples
- o Pray
- o Love
- o Worship
- o Joy
- o Repent

- o Believe
- o Faith
- o Bible
- o World
- o Father
- o Son
- o Amen
- o Grace
- o Saved
- o Sin

QUESTIONS I HAVE:

SERMON TITLE:

SERMON NOTES:

DATE:

MY FAVORITE SONG TODAY:

WORDS I DID NOT UNDERSTAND:

I AM THANKFUL FOR:

THIS WEEK, I WILL PRAY FOR:

TODAY'S SCRIPTURE PASSAGE:

I LEFT CHURCH FEELING:

THIS WEEK, I WILL:
(write something you learned today that you can apply to your life this week)

CREATIVE SPACE

WORDS I HEARD THE PASTOR SAY:
(CHECK ONCE OR EACH TIME YOU HEAR IT)

- o God
- o Jesus
- o Holy Spirit
- o Church
- o Disciples
- o Pray
- o Love
- o Worship
- o Joy
- o Repent

- o Believe
- o Faith
- o Bible
- o World
- o Father
- o Son
- o Amen
- o Grace
- o Saved
- o Sin

QUESTIONS I HAVE:

SERMON TITLE:

SERMON NOTES:

DATE:

MY FAVORITE SONG TODAY:

WORDS I DID NOT UNDERSTAND:

I AM THANKFUL FOR:

THIS WEEK, I WILL PRAY FOR:

TODAY'S SCRIPTURE PASSAGE:

I LEFT CHURCH FEELING:

THIS WEEK, I WILL:
(write something you learned today that
you can apply to your life this week)

CREATIVE SPACE

WORDS I HEARD THE PASTOR SAY:
(CHECK ONCE OR EACH TIME YOU HEAR IT)

- ○ God
- ○ Jesus
- ○ Holy Spirit
- ○ Church
- ○ Disciples
- ○ Pray
- ○ Love
- ○ Worship
- ○ Joy
- ○ Repent

- ○ Believe
- ○ Faith
- ○ Bible
- ○ World
- ○ Father
- ○ Son
- ○ Amen
- ○ Grace
- ○ Saved
- ○ Sin

QUESTIONS I HAVE:

SERMON TITLE:

SERMON NOTES:

DATE:

MY FAVORITE SONG TODAY:

WORDS I DID NOT UNDERSTAND:

I AM THANKFUL FOR:

THIS WEEK, I WILL PRAY FOR:

TODAY'S SCRIPTURE PASSAGE:

I LEFT CHURCH FEELING:

THIS WEEK, I WILL:
(write something you learned today that you can apply to your life this week)

CREATIVE SPACE

WORDS I HEARD THE PASTOR SAY:
(CHECK ONCE OR EACH TIME YOU HEAR IT)

- ○ God
- ○ Jesus
- ○ Holy Spirit
- ○ Church
- ○ Disciples
- ○ Pray
- ○ Love
- ○ Worship
- ○ Joy
- ○ Repent
- ○ Believe
- ○ Faith
- ○ Bible
- ○ World
- ○ Father
- ○ Son
- ○ Amen
- ○ Grace
- ○ Saved
- ○ Sin

QUESTIONS I HAVE:

SERMON TITLE:

SERMON NOTES:

DATE:

MY FAVORITE SONG TODAY:

WORDS I DID NOT UNDERSTAND:

I AM THANKFUL FOR:

THIS WEEK, I WILL PRAY FOR:

TODAY'S SCRIPTURE PASSAGE:

I LEFT CHURCH FEELING:

THIS WEEK, I WILL:
(write something you learned today that you can apply to your life this week)

CREATIVE SPACE

WORDS I HEARD THE PASTOR SAY:
(CHECK ONCE OR EACH TIME YOU HEAR IT)

- O God
- O Jesus
- O Holy Spirit
- O Church
- O Disciples
- O Pray
- O Love
- O Worship
- O Joy
- O Repent

- O Believe
- O Faith
- O Bible
- O World
- O Father
- O Son
- O Amen
- O Grace
- O Saved
- O Sin

QUESTIONS I HAVE:

SERMON TITLE:

SERMON NOTES:

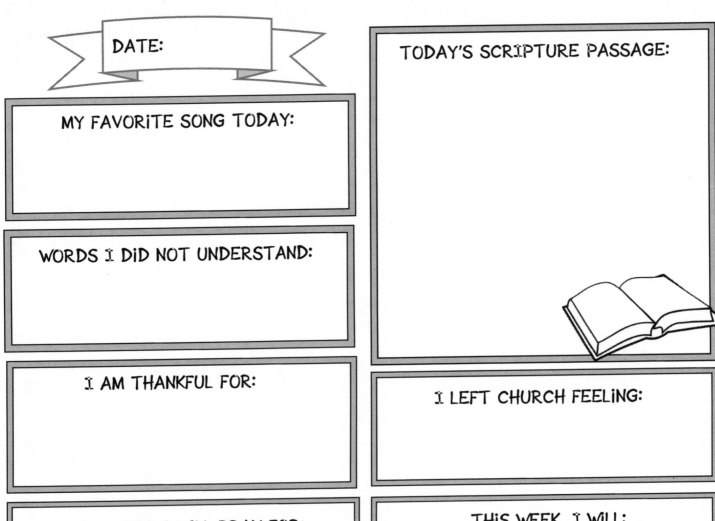

DATE:

MY FAVORITE SONG TODAY:

WORDS I DID NOT UNDERSTAND:

I AM THANKFUL FOR:

THIS WEEK, I WILL PRAY FOR:

TODAY'S SCRIPTURE PASSAGE:

I LEFT CHURCH FEELING:

THIS WEEK, I WILL:
(write something you learned today that
you can apply to your life this week)

CREATIVE SPACE

WORDS I HEARD THE PASTOR SAY:
(CHECK ONCE OR EACH TIME YOU HEAR IT)

- o God
- o Jesus
- o Holy Spirit
- o Church
- o Disciples
- o Pray
- o Love
- o Worship
- o Joy
- o Repent

- o Believe
- o Faith
- o Bible
- o World
- o Father
- o Son
- o Amen
- o Grace
- o Saved
- o Sin

QUESTIONS I HAVE:

SERMON TITLE:

SERMON NOTES:

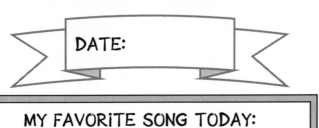

DATE:

MY FAVORITE SONG TODAY:

WORDS I DID NOT UNDERSTAND:

I AM THANKFUL FOR:

THIS WEEK, I WILL PRAY FOR:

TODAY'S SCRIPTURE PASSAGE:

I LEFT CHURCH FEELING:

THIS WEEK, I WILL:
(write something you learned today that you can apply to your life this week)

CREATIVE SPACE

WORDS I HEARD THE PASTOR SAY:
(CHECK ONCE OR EACH TIME YOU HEAR IT)

- ○ God
- ○ Jesus
- ○ Holy Spirit
- ○ Church
- ○ Disciples
- ○ Pray
- ○ Love
- ○ Worship
- ○ Joy
- ○ Repent

- ○ Believe
- ○ Faith
- ○ Bible
- ○ World
- ○ Father
- ○ Son
- ○ Amen
- ○ Grace
- ○ Saved
- ○ Sin

QUESTIONS I HAVE:

SERMON TITLE:

SERMON NOTES:

DATE:

MY FAVORITE SONG TODAY:

WORDS I DID NOT UNDERSTAND:

I AM THANKFUL FOR:

THIS WEEK, I WILL PRAY FOR:

TODAY'S SCRIPTURE PASSAGE:

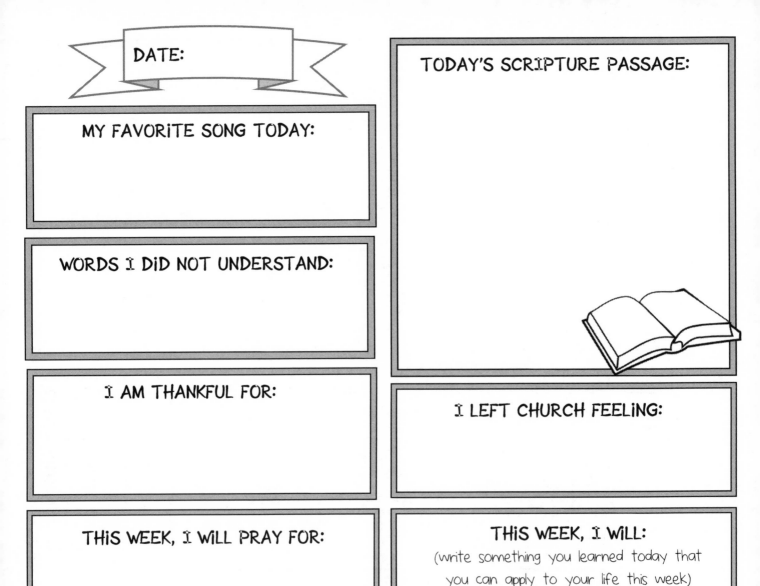

I LEFT CHURCH FEELING:

THIS WEEK, I WILL:
(write something you learned today that you can apply to your life this week)

CREATIVE SPACE

WORDS I HEARD THE PASTOR SAY:
(CHECK ONCE OR EACH TIME YOU HEAR IT)

- ○ God
- ○ Jesus
- ○ Holy Spirit
- ○ Church
- ○ Disciples
- ○ Pray
- ○ Love
- ○ Worship
- ○ Joy
- ○ Repent

- ○ Believe
- ○ Faith
- ○ Bible
- ○ World
- ○ Father
- ○ Son
- ○ Amen
- ○ Grace
- ○ Saved
- ○ Sin

QUESTIONS I HAVE:

SERMON TITLE:

SERMON NOTES:

DATE:

MY FAVORITE SONG TODAY:

WORDS I DID NOT UNDERSTAND:

I AM THANKFUL FOR:

THIS WEEK, I WILL PRAY FOR:

TODAY'S SCRIPTURE PASSAGE:

I LEFT CHURCH FEELING:

THIS WEEK, I WILL:
(write something you learned today that you can apply to your life this week)

CREATIVE SPACE

WORDS I HEARD THE PASTOR SAY:
(CHECK ONCE OR EACH TIME YOU HEAR IT)

- ○ God
- ○ Jesus
- ○ Holy Spirit
- ○ Church
- ○ Disciples
- ○ Pray
- ○ Love
- ○ Worship
- ○ Joy
- ○ Repent

- ○ Believe
- ○ Faith
- ○ Bible
- ○ World
- ○ Father
- ○ Son
- ○ Amen
- ○ Grace
- ○ Saved
- ○ Sin

QUESTIONS I HAVE:

SERMON TITLE:

SERMON NOTES:

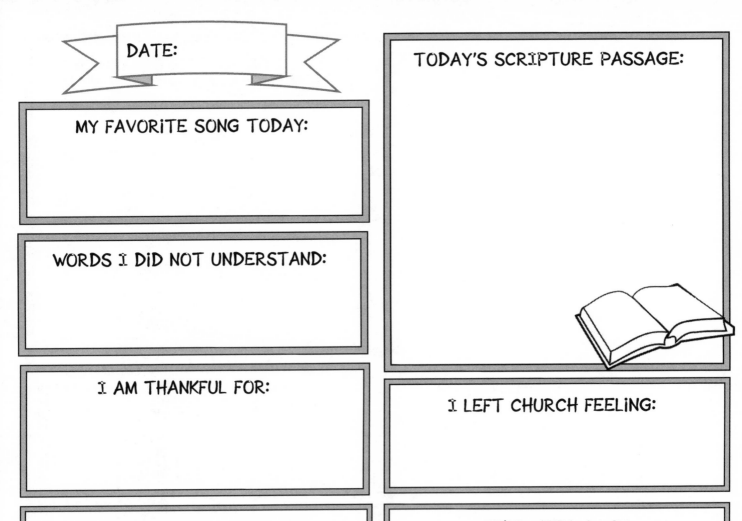

DATE:

MY FAVORITE SONG TODAY:

WORDS I DID NOT UNDERSTAND:

I AM THANKFUL FOR:

THIS WEEK, I WILL PRAY FOR:

TODAY'S SCRIPTURE PASSAGE:

I LEFT CHURCH FEELING:

THIS WEEK, I WILL:
(write something you learned today that you can apply to your life this week)

CREATIVE SPACE

WORDS I HEARD THE PASTOR SAY:
(CHECK ONCE OR EACH TIME YOU HEAR IT)

- ○ God
- ○ Jesus
- ○ Holy Spirit
- ○ Church
- ○ Disciples
- ○ Pray
- ○ Love
- ○ Worship
- ○ Joy
- ○ Repent

- ○ Believe
- ○ Faith
- ○ Bible
- ○ World
- ○ Father
- ○ Son
- ○ Amen
- ○ Grace
- ○ Saved
- ○ Sin

QUESTIONS I HAVE:

SERMON TITLE:

SERMON NOTES:

DATE:

MY FAVORITE SONG TODAY:

WORDS I DID NOT UNDERSTAND:

I AM THANKFUL FOR:

THIS WEEK, I WILL PRAY FOR:

TODAY'S SCRIPTURE PASSAGE:

I LEFT CHURCH FEELING:

THIS WEEK, I WILL:
(write something you learned today that you can apply to your life this week)

CREATIVE SPACE

WORDS I HEARD THE PASTOR SAY:
(CHECK ONCE OR EACH TIME YOU HEAR IT)

- ○ God
- ○ Jesus
- ○ Holy Spirit
- ○ Church
- ○ Disciples
- ○ Pray
- ○ Love
- ○ Worship
- ○ Joy
- ○ Repent
- ○ Believe
- ○ Faith
- ○ Bible
- ○ World
- ○ Father
- ○ Son
- ○ Amen
- ○ Grace
- ○ Saved
- ○ Sin

QUESTIONS I HAVE:

SERMON TITLE:

SERMON NOTES:

MY FAVORITE SONG TODAY:

TODAY'S SCRIPTURE PASSAGE:

WORDS I DID NOT UNDERSTAND:

I AM THANKFUL FOR:

I LEFT CHURCH FEELING:

THIS WEEK, I WILL PRAY FOR:

THIS WEEK, I WILL:
(write something you learned today that you can apply to your life this week)

CREATIVE SPACE

WORDS I HEARD THE PASTOR SAY:
(CHECK ONCE OR EACH TIME YOU HEAR IT)

- ○ God
- ○ Jesus
- ○ Holy Spirit
- ○ Church
- ○ Disciples
- ○ Pray
- ○ Love
- ○ Worship
- ○ Joy
- ○ Repent

- ○ Believe
- ○ Faith
- ○ Bible
- ○ World
- ○ Father
- ○ Son
- ○ Amen
- ○ Grace
- ○ Saved
- ○ Sin

QUESTIONS I HAVE:

SERMON TITLE:

SERMON NOTES:

DATE:

MY FAVORITE SONG TODAY:

WORDS I DID NOT UNDERSTAND:

I AM THANKFUL FOR:

THIS WEEK, I WILL PRAY FOR:

TODAY'S SCRIPTURE PASSAGE:

I LEFT CHURCH FEELING:

THIS WEEK, I WILL:
(write something you learned today that
you can apply to your life this week)

CREATIVE SPACE

WORDS I HEARD THE PASTOR SAY:
(CHECK ONCE OR EACH TIME YOU HEAR IT)

- o God
- o Jesus
- o Holy Spirit
- o Church
- o Disciples
- o Pray
- o Love
- o Worship
- o Joy
- o Repent

- o Believe
- o Faith
- o Bible
- o World
- o Father
- o Son
- o Amen
- o Grace
- o Saved
- o Sin

QUESTIONS I HAVE:

SERMON TITLE:

SERMON NOTES:

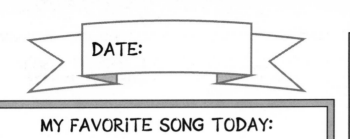

DATE:

MY FAVORITE SONG TODAY:

WORDS I DID NOT UNDERSTAND:

I AM THANKFUL FOR:

THIS WEEK, I WILL PRAY FOR:

TODAY'S SCRIPTURE PASSAGE:

I LEFT CHURCH FEELING:

THIS WEEK, I WILL:
(write something you learned today that you can apply to your life this week)

CREATIVE SPACE

WORDS I HEARD THE PASTOR SAY:
(CHECK ONCE OR EACH TIME YOU HEAR IT)

- ○ God
- ○ Jesus
- ○ Holy Spirit
- ○ Church
- ○ Disciples
- ○ Pray
- ○ Love
- ○ Worship
- ○ Joy
- ○ Repent

- ○ Believe
- ○ Faith
- ○ Bible
- ○ World
- ○ Father
- ○ Son
- ○ Amen
- ○ Grace
- ○ Saved
- ○ Sin

QUESTIONS I HAVE:

SERMON TITLE:

SERMON NOTES:

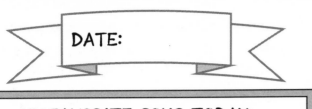

DATE:

MY FAVORITE SONG TODAY:

WORDS I DID NOT UNDERSTAND:

I AM THANKFUL FOR:

THIS WEEK, I WILL PRAY FOR:

TODAY'S SCRIPTURE PASSAGE:

I LEFT CHURCH FEELING:

THIS WEEK, I WILL:
(write something you learned today that you can apply to your life this week)

CREATIVE SPACE

WORDS I HEARD THE PASTOR SAY:
(CHECK ONCE OR EACH TIME YOU HEAR IT)

- ○ God
- ○ Jesus
- ○ Holy Spirit
- ○ Church
- ○ Disciples
- ○ Pray
- ○ Love
- ○ Worship
- ○ Joy
- ○ Repent

- ○ Believe
- ○ Faith
- ○ Bible
- ○ World
- ○ Father
- ○ Son
- ○ Amen
- ○ Grace
- ○ Saved
- ○ Sin

QUESTIONS I HAVE:

SERMON TITLE:

SERMON NOTES:

DATE:

MY FAVORITE SONG TODAY:

WORDS I DID NOT UNDERSTAND:

I AM THANKFUL FOR:

THIS WEEK, I WILL PRAY FOR:

TODAY'S SCRIPTURE PASSAGE:

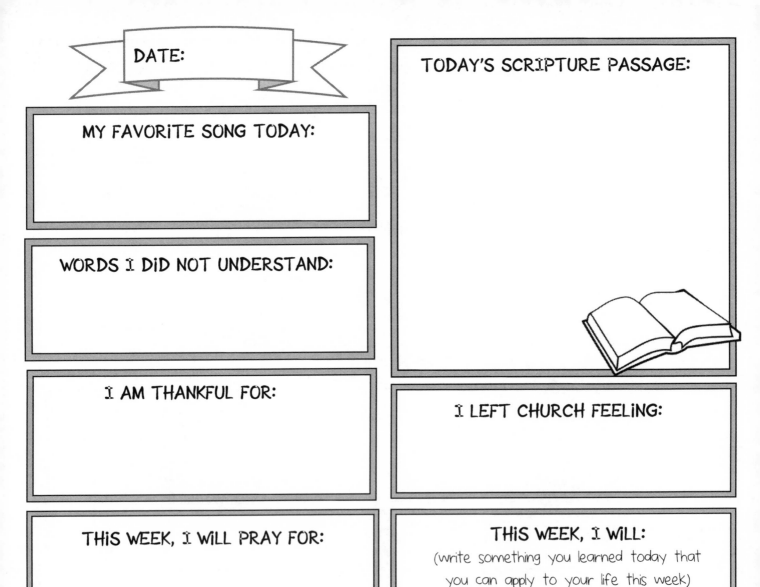

I LEFT CHURCH FEELING:

THIS WEEK, I WILL:
(write something you learned today that you can apply to your life this week)

CREATIVE SPACE

WORDS I HEARD THE PASTOR SAY:
(CHECK ONCE OR EACH TIME YOU HEAR IT)

- O God
- O Jesus
- O Holy Spirit
- O Church
- O Disciples
- O Pray
- O Love
- O Worship
- O Joy
- O Repent

- O Believe
- O Faith
- O Bible
- O World
- O Father
- O Son
- O Amen
- O Grace
- O Saved
- O Sin

QUESTIONS I HAVE:

SERMON TITLE:

SERMON NOTES:

DATE:

MY FAVORITE SONG TODAY:

WORDS I DID NOT UNDERSTAND:

I AM THANKFUL FOR:

THIS WEEK, I WILL PRAY FOR:

TODAY'S SCRIPTURE PASSAGE:

I LEFT CHURCH FEELING:

THIS WEEK, I WILL:
(write something you learned today that
you can apply to your life this week)

CREATIVE SPACE

WORDS I HEARD THE PASTOR SAY:
(CHECK ONCE OR EACH TIME YOU HEAR IT)

- ○ God
- ○ Jesus
- ○ Holy Spirit
- ○ Church
- ○ Disciples
- ○ Pray
- ○ Love
- ○ Worship
- ○ Joy
- ○ Repent

- ○ Believe
- ○ Faith
- ○ Bible
- ○ World
- ○ Father
- ○ Son
- ○ Amen
- ○ Grace
- ○ Saved
- ○ Sin

QUESTIONS I HAVE:

SERMON TITLE:

SERMON NOTES:

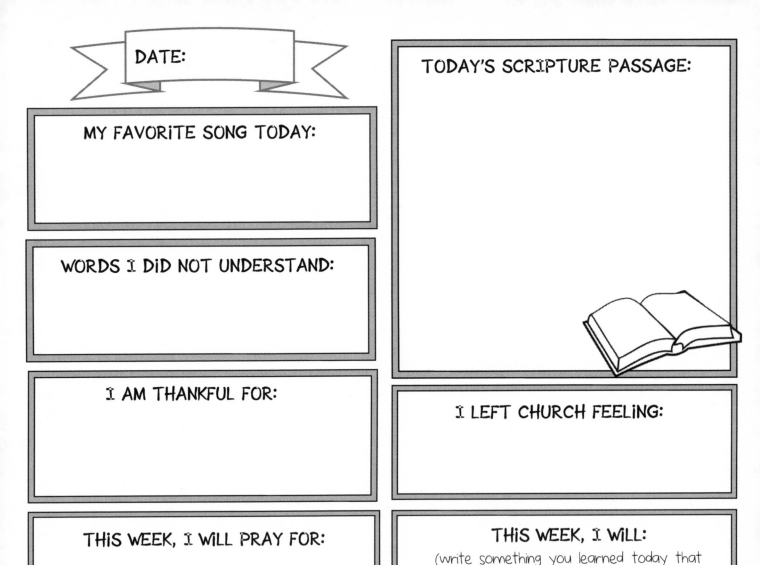

DATE:

MY FAVORITE SONG TODAY:

WORDS I DID NOT UNDERSTAND:

I AM THANKFUL FOR:

THIS WEEK, I WILL PRAY FOR:

TODAY'S SCRIPTURE PASSAGE:

I LEFT CHURCH FEELING:

THIS WEEK, I WILL:
(write something you learned today that you can apply to your life this week)

CREATIVE SPACE

WORDS I HEARD THE PASTOR SAY:
(CHECK ONCE OR EACH TIME YOU HEAR IT)

- o God
- o Jesus
- o Holy Spirit
- o Church
- o Disciples
- o Pray
- o Love
- o Worship
- o Joy
- o Repent
- o Believe
- o Faith
- o Bible
- o World
- o Father
- o Son
- o Amen
- o Grace
- o Saved
- o Sin

QUESTIONS I HAVE:

SERMON TITLE:

SERMON NOTES:

DATE:

MY FAVORITE SONG TODAY:

WORDS I DID NOT UNDERSTAND:

I AM THANKFUL FOR:

THIS WEEK, I WILL PRAY FOR:

TODAY'S SCRIPTURE PASSAGE:

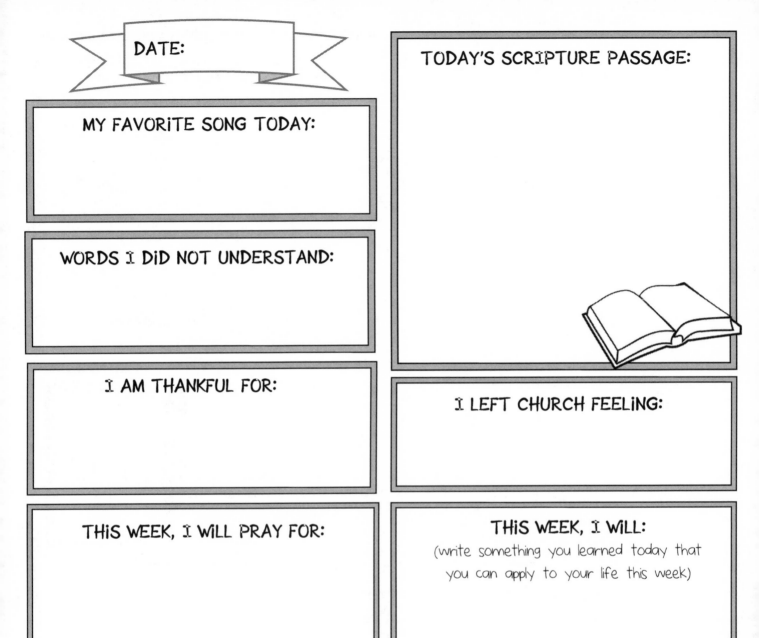

I LEFT CHURCH FEELING:

THIS WEEK, I WILL:
(write something you learned today that you can apply to your life this week)

CREATIVE SPACE

WORDS I HEARD THE PASTOR SAY:
(CHECK ONCE OR EACH TIME YOU HEAR IT)

- o God
- o Jesus
- o Holy Spirit
- o Church
- o Disciples
- o Pray
- o Love
- o Worship
- o Joy
- o Repent

- o Believe
- o Faith
- o Bible
- o World
- o Father
- o Son
- o Amen
- o Grace
- o Saved
- o Sin

QUESTIONS I HAVE:

SERMON TITLE:

SERMON NOTES:

DATE:

MY FAVORITE SONG TODAY:

WORDS I DID NOT UNDERSTAND:

I AM THANKFUL FOR:

THIS WEEK, I WILL PRAY FOR:

TODAY'S SCRIPTURE PASSAGE:

I LEFT CHURCH FEELING:

THIS WEEK, I WILL:
(write something you learned today that you can apply to your life this week)

CREATIVE SPACE

WORDS I HEARD THE PASTOR SAY:
(CHECK ONCE OR EACH TIME YOU HEAR IT)

- O God
- O Jesus
- O Holy Spirit
- O Church
- O Disciples
- O Pray
- O Love
- O Worship
- O Joy
- O Repent

- O Believe
- O Faith
- O Bible
- O World
- O Father
- O Son
- O Amen
- O Grace
- O Saved
- O Sin

QUESTIONS I HAVE:

SERMON TITLE:

SERMON NOTES:

DATE:

MY FAVORITE SONG TODAY:

WORDS I DID NOT UNDERSTAND:

I AM THANKFUL FOR:

THIS WEEK, I WILL PRAY FOR:

TODAY'S SCRIPTURE PASSAGE:

I LEFT CHURCH FEELING:

THIS WEEK, I WILL:
(write something you learned today that you can apply to your life this week)

CREATIVE SPACE

WORDS I HEARD THE PASTOR SAY:
(CHECK ONCE OR EACH TIME YOU HEAR IT)

- ○ God
- ○ Jesus
- ○ Holy Spirit
- ○ Church
- ○ Disciples
- ○ Pray
- ○ Love
- ○ Worship
- ○ Joy
- ○ Repent

- ○ Believe
- ○ Faith
- ○ Bible
- ○ World
- ○ Father
- ○ Son
- ○ Amen
- ○ Grace
- ○ Saved
- ○ Sin

QUESTIONS I HAVE:

SERMON TITLE:

SERMON NOTES:

How many smaller words can you make from the word...

OMNISCIENT

○ _____   ○ _____
○ _____   ○ _____
○ _____   ○ _____
○ _____   ○ _____
○ _____   ○ _____
○ _____   ○ _____
○ _____   ○ _____
○ _____   ○ _____
○ _____   ○ _____
○ _____   ○ _____
○ _____   ○ _____
○ _____   ○ _____
○ _____   ○ _____
○ _____   ○ _____
○ _____   ○ _____

Definition: All knowing. Refers to God, the one who knows and sees all.

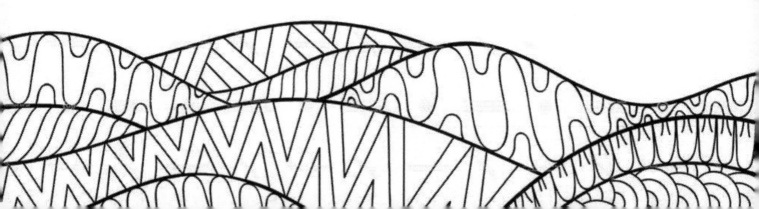

How many smaller words can you make from the word...

OMNIPRESENT

○ _____   ○ _____
○ _____   ○ _____
○ _____   ○ _____
○ _____   ○ _____
○ _____   ○ _____
○ _____   ○ _____
○ _____   ○ _____
○ _____   ○ _____
○ _____   ○ _____
○ _____   ○ _____
○ _____   ○ _____
○ _____   ○ _____
○ _____   ○ _____
○ _____   ○ _____
○ _____   ○ _____

Definition: Everywhere, all present. Refers to God who surrounds us, is always near.

How many smaller words can you make from the word...

JUSTIFICATION

○ _____   ○ _____
○ _____   ○ _____
○ _____   ○ _____
○ _____   ○ _____
○ _____   ○ _____
○ _____   ○ _____
○ _____   ○ _____
○ _____   ○ _____
○ _____   ○ _____
○ _____   ○ _____
○ _____   ○ _____
○ _____   ○ _____
○ _____   ○ _____
○ _____   ○ _____
○ _____   ○ _____

Definition: being made acceptable to God through Jesus Christ's death. Jesus paid the debt that we owed God for all our sins.

How many smaller words can you make from the word...

RESURRECTION

○ _____   ○ _____

○ _____   ○ _____

○ _____   ○ _____

○ _____   ○ _____

○ _____   ○ _____

○ _____   ○ _____

○ _____   ○ _____

○ _____   ○ _____

○ _____   ○ _____

○ _____   ○ _____

○ _____   ○ _____

○ _____   ○ _____

○ _____   ○ _____

○ _____   ○ _____

○ _____   ○ _____

Definition: To be raised up, as Jesus was raised from the dead

How many smaller words can you make from the word...

SANCTIFICATION

○ _____   ○ _____
○ _____   ○ _____
○ _____   ○ _____
○ _____   ○ _____
○ _____   ○ _____
○ _____   ○ _____
○ _____   ○ _____
○ _____   ○ _____
○ _____   ○ _____
○ _____   ○ _____
○ _____   ○ _____
○ _____   ○ _____
○ _____   ○ _____
○ _____   ○ _____
○ _____   ○ _____

Definition: The process of being made holy, or Christ-like through the Holy Spirit.

How many smaller words can you make from the word...

INTERCESSION

○ _____   ○ _____
○ _____   ○ _____
○ _____   ○ _____
○ _____   ○ _____
○ _____   ○ _____
○ _____   ○ _____
○ _____   ○ _____
○ _____   ○ _____
○ _____   ○ _____
○ _____   ○ _____
○ _____   ○ _____
○ _____   ○ _____
○ _____   ○ _____
○ _____   ○ _____
○ _____   ○ _____

Definition: to intervene for someone, such as Jesus Christ who is the
mediator between man and God.

How many smaller words can you make from the word...

COMMUNICATE

○ _____   ○ _____
○ _____   ○ _____
○ _____   ○ _____
○ _____   ○ _____
○ _____   ○ _____
○ _____   ○ _____
○ _____   ○ _____
○ _____   ○ _____
○ _____   ○ _____
○ _____   ○ _____
○ _____   ○ _____
○ _____   ○ _____
○ _____   ○ _____
○ _____   ○ _____
○ _____   ○ _____

Definition: To interact with another being by different means- can include words, expressions, gestures, body language and tone of voice.

www.wildrose-media.com

Email us at wildrosemedia18@gmail.com for special requests,
to leave a review, comment, or to join our mailing list.

YOU MIGHT ALSO ENJOY THESE BOOKS, AVAILABLE ON AMAZON:
- more books coming soon-subscribe to our mailing list for alerts!

Bible Coloring Pages (also available for download from our website):
Delight in God's Word- KJV Bible Verses to Color
     ISBN: 978-1-953489-00-5
Delight in God's Word- NIV Bible Verses to Color
     ISBN: 978-1-953489-01-2

The Books of the Bible Summary Pages: (also available for download from our website)
Bible Book Teaching Sheets: The New Testament, KJV Edition- Book-by-Book Summaries, Key Verses, and Background Information for all 27 books of the New Testament
     ISBN: 978-1-953489-05-0
Bible Book Teaching Sheets: The New Testament, NIV Edition- Book-by-Book Summaries, Key Verses, and Background Information for all 27 books of the New Testament
     ISBN: 978-1-953489-04-3

Word Searches:
Christian Word Search Puzzles and Coloring Book: The Bible People and Places
     Large Print Edition (8.5" x 11") ISBN: 978-1-953489-06-7
Christian Word Search Puzzles and Coloring Book: The Bible from A to Z
     Large Print Edition (8.5" x 11") ISBN: 978-1-953489-07-4
Find-A-Word, Word Search Puzzles and Coloring Book Volume 1
     Large Print Edition (8.5" x 11") ISBN:978-1-953489-11-1
Find-A-Word, Word Search Puzzles and Coloring Book Volume 2
     Large Print Edition (8.5" x 11") ISBN: 978-1-953489-12-8

scan QR above for direct link to our website shop on wildrose-media.com

Prayer Journal:
ISBN: 978-1-953489-08-1

Sermon Notebooks for Kids
Simple Sermon Notes for Kids ages 6-8
     ISBN: 978-1-953489-09-8
My Sermon Notebook for Kids ages 6-8
     ISBN: 978-1-953489-14-2

scan QR above for more great books on our Amazon Author Page!

Sermon Notebooks for Men and Women
     6" x 9", floral cover ISBN: 978-1791340957
     6" x 9", beach scene cover ISBN: 978-1791602086

Made in the USA
Columbia, SC
21 October 2020